WORKBOOK

FOR

UNDO IT!

HOW SIMPLE LIFESTYLE CHANGES
CAN REVERSE MOST CHRONIC DISEASES

By
**Dean Ornish M.D. and
Anne Ornish**

PockeTBooks

Table of Contents

HOW TO USE THE WORKBOOK...4

INTRODUCTION...5

CHAPTER ONE: IT WORKS 6

   LESSONS AND TAKEAWAYS..6

CHAPTER TWO: WHY IT WORKS 11

CHAPTER THREE: THE LIFESTYLE MEDICINE REVOLUTION 15

   LESSONS AND TAKEAWAYS...15

CHAPTER FOUR: EAT WELL 20

   LESSONS AND TAKEAWAYS...20

CHAPTER FIVE: MOVE MORE 25

   LESSONS AND TAKEAWAYS...25

CHAPTER SIX: STRESS LESS 30

   LESSONS & TAKEAWAYS 30

CHAPTER SEVEN: LOVE MORE 34

   LESSONS AND TAKEAWAYS...34

CHAPTER EIGHT: THE ORNISH KITCHEN/ TRUE LOVE RECIPES ..38

HOW TO USE THE WORKBOOK

This workbook is created to help readers grasp a deeper understanding of Undo It! by going a step further than simply reading. The book proffers a lifestyle change program for the reversal of most chronic diseases and it is only fitting that certain practical steps be put in place by the reader. This workbook provides that.

The lessons outline essential points offered by the authors, Dean Ornish and Anne Ornish, while questions crafted from each chapter help the reader look inward and discover where their lives stand in relation to the book's position.

Action Steps keep you on your toes with putting the book's theory into practice and if you need something to tick off as you progress, there's the Checklist section.

At the end of it all, you should be able to have successfully implemented the lifestyle medicine program proposed in this phenomenal book.

INTRODUCTION

Undo It! by Dean Ornish and Anne Ornish proposes a science-based and love-oriented approach to reversing most chronic diseases and at the center of it is the insistent call to change your lifestyle if you want to change your health.

This accompanying workbook aids you in your quest to fulfilling the highlighted steps and suggestions in Undo It!, making sure the book does not become just another conquest in your library.

It may seem like a lot, but if you faithfully follow this workbook, there's only good to be found by the time you hit the last page.

All the best!

CHAPTER ONE: IT WORKS

If you're still in doubt as to whether this stuff works or not, you're not in the wrong. It's very understandable. Many of us grew up learning about healthy eating and balanced diets, consuming animal based protein as a norm and feeding on the things that indirectly kill us. But hey! It's no fault of yours. Society preached this, and so did the classrooms. The internet is filled with all of these, and the regular medical practice didn't state otherwise. So yeah, you've caught the bug, and you now have a heart disease, despite eating 'healthily' and doing all the right things. It sucks! But you can right this wrong. You got here by no fault of yours. However, you can give yourself the healthy, beautiful, glowing life you deserve; right now, right here! And if you ignore this, then it is your fault!

LESSONS AND TAKEAWAYS

- You might find it difficult, at first, to believe in the efficacy of lifestyle medicine. But you have to trust that this is what you need, for your health and better life. Somehow, we think we know what's best for us, but we do not. You might want to consider this. You've been hung up on these drugs for quite a while. And yeah, you're alive, but you do not feel better. That should suggest to you that something is wrong. You do not want to simply exist; you want to live.

- Accept that the switch might not be easy at first; especially because it's entirely different from what you're used to. Do it anyway!

- Awareness is important. Be aware that you CAN be healed! Disallow skepticism and connect with the inner you.

- You need to know that you stand to gain a lot, in the sense that the quality of your life and health will improve, and you wouldn't spend half as much as you probably would, consuming drugs.

- Know that your life ought to be enjoyed, not endured. And with this program, you can have just that!

QUESTIONS

1. What do you say about your health?

_____

_____

_____

_____

2. What health- related decisions did you take in the past?

_____

_____

_____

_____

3. Where did you think your regular diet and health lifestyle would lead you?

_____

_____

_____

_____

4. What do you think about your heath now?

_____

_____

_____

_____

5. Do you think you deserve to live healthily, and meaningfully?

_____

_____

_____

_____

6. Why do you think you'd never live a life of health, fun and joy?

_____

_____

_____

_____

7. Are you willing to help yourself?

_____

_____

_____

_____

ACTION STEPS

- Acknowledge your health status. If you're healthy, be happy. If you have a chronic disease, there's hope.
- Resolve within yourself to help your life, by living healthy.
- Be ready to love. Give love and receive love. Your health needs it.
- Be open to your doctors. Allow them go on this journey with you. Your health will thank you.

CHECKLIST

- You cannot afford to lose hope. You will be healed!

- Condition your mind to go through with the process. Others have done this, and so will you.
- Prepare to be rejuvenated. Expect your health to take a turn for the best.
- Laugh, smile and don't forget to live!

CHAPTER TWO: WHY IT WORKS

The lifestyle medicine program was like any other idea brought into existence.

Today, it has become a ground-breaking source of joy and hope for many. It can become a testimony for you as well.

Take a chance on it. It works, and there is a reason why it does. Most chronic diseases were all birthed from similar root causes, mechanisms and pathways, making it seemingly easy to reverse each and every one of them, through the same lifestyle change.

Living healthy just got better!

LESSONS AND TAKEAWAYS

- This program met with doubts and criticisms when it just began, until there were results to prove its efficacy. Do not be deceived. You would realize eventually that realize that it is a beautiful idea after all.

- The program is hinged on these four things- Eating right, exercising moderately, reducing stress and loving better. Do them as you should, and your health would take a turn.

- It is very possible to reverse diseases. However, it requires a lot more lifestyle changes than preventing the diseases do.

- You can change your genes- they are not your fate!

QUESTIONS

1. Describe what you know about this disease and how it makes you feel.

_____

_____

_____

_____

2. Have you tried to seek medical attention?

_____

_____

3. How have you responded to treatment, so far?

_____

_____

_____

_____

4. Are you happy with your health status now?

_____

_____

_____

_____

5. Do you believe that this disease(s) can be gone, and kept at bay forever?

_____

_____

_____

_____

6. Do you blame the disease(s) on the genes handed down to you by your parents?

_____

_____

_____

_____

7. Are you ready to change your lifestyle?

_____

_____

_____

_____

ACTION STEPS

- From today onwards, choose to live in love and intimacy.
- Exercise daily by taking a walk for just twenty minutes. You reduce inflammation this way.
- Decide today to let go of unhealthy protein. Bit by bit, replace all your animal based protein with plant based proteins.

CHECKLIST

- Do not think this is impossible. You will not just survive, you'll live!
- The removal of unhealthy meals from your diet is not the end of you. It's not starvation either. It is the beginning of a healthier, stronger, you.
- As you journey through the day, be conscious of what you choose to feed your mind with. Remember, you need to stay emotionally balanced. Do what you love, and be around those that make you happy.

CHAPTER THREE: THE LIFESTYLE MEDICINE REVOLUTION

Lifestyle medicine is here, right on time. As the wonders of this program spread, the world remains continually shocked by the realization of how limiting the 'almighty' high-tech medicine is. And more than anything, grateful hearts rent the air, in thankfulness that lifestyle medicine is here, at a time like this!

The desire of many physicians to see people healed caused them to study the medical profession. Yet, the conventional medicine has failed to restore hope, health and vitality to many.

But there is good news! Lifestyle changes offer better results than drugs or surgeries ever would. And this is all that you need to run with!

LESSONS AND TAKEAWAYS
- Heart diseases are best reversed or slowed down using lifestyle medicine. Stents and angioplasties are limited in functionality.

- By following the lifestyle medicine program, you can completely prevent Type 2 Diabetes. How cool!

- Employing surgery and radiation in the treatment of prostate cancer does not guarantee longer lives than those who do not.

- In many cases, the root causes of these diseases are related to your lifestyle. Hence, they can be treated and reversed using lifestyle medicine.

QUESTIONS

1. How do you feel knowing that lifestyle medicine can do more than drugs or surgeries?

_____

_____

_____

_____

2. What are your fears about lifestyle medicine and your health status? Write them out.

_____

_____

_____

_____

3. Close your eyes. Are these fears worth having?

_____

_____

_____

_____

4. Think about the answers you provided in Question
   (3). Are they valid?

   _____

   _____

   _____

   _____

5. Close your eyes again. Now imagine the worst that
   could happen. Write it out.

   _____

   _____

   _____

   _____

   _____

   _____

   _____

   _____

   _____

6. Like you did in (5) above, imagine yourself in the best of health and strength. How does that make you feel?

_____

_____

_____

_____

7. Do you have prostate cancer?

_____

8. Do you think that lifestyle medicine can help you get well again?

_____

_____

_____

_____

ACTION STEPS

- Consume whole-foods, plant based diet.
- Make good lifestyle choices to avoid developing prostate cancer

CHECKLIST

- Drugs and surgeries can equally save lives. They can be infused alongside lifestyle changes.
- You must address the root cause of the disease- your lifestyle choices.

CHAPTER FOUR: EAT WELL

Have you noticed that when it comes to diet and nutrition, everyone has an opinion? It's so easy to get swarmed in a myriad of advises, teachings and opinions about what, when and how to eat. In a situation like this, being grateful is in order as the lifestyle medicine program has come just in time to liberate you from the hold of false, half- baked nutrition based teachings.

Day after day, many are coming to the realization of the healthiest way to eat, through the consumption of whole foods, plant-based diet. What's more? This diet is capable of reversing the development of many chronic diseases.

Wouldn't you rather eat and live?

LESSONS AND TAKEAWAYS
- The foods you decide to eat are as important as though you choose to avoid. Choose wisely!
- Avoid animal protein.
- Meat won't help you garner as much strength as plant-based diets would.
- Eat only plants. They contain good carbs and good fat.

QUESTIONS

1. Prior to getting to know about the lifestyle medicine program, what was your opinion about nutrition?

   _____

   _____

   _____

   _____

2. Now that you are sufficiently knowledgeable about the lifestyle medicine program, what has changed about your opinion about nutrition?

   _____

   _____

   _____

   _____

3. How do you intend on achieving the best results with your health?

   _____

   _____

   _____

   _____

   _____

   _____

   _____

4. Look at the list of plant based sources of proteins in this book. Which ones do you think you can consume to obtain the essential amino acids?

_____

_____

_____

_____

_____

_____

_____

_____

5. How often do you eat meat?

_____

_____

_____

_____

6. Are you willing to give up the consumption of animal protein?

_____

_____

_____

_____

7. Close your eyes. Imagine eating what you love, feeling good and enjoying your life. How did that make you feel? Write it out.

_____

_____

_____

_____

_____

_____

_____

8. Are you willing to do what it takes to achieve the life described in (7) above?

_____

_____

_____

_____

ACTION STEPS

- Gradually begin to reduce your consumption of animal protein.

- Make sure your meals contain plant based foods in varying proportions.
- Take note of how you feel after each plant based meal. It'll help you sustain the program.

CHECKLIST

- Avoid plant-based foods that contain high fat levels.
- Consume nuts in small quantities, your cardio life needs this.

CHAPTER FIVE: MOVE MORE

You must have heard a lot about how good exercise is for you. But I bet you have no idea the amazing benefits that lay in wait for you, by engaging in the tiniest bits of exercise. As for as long as you love the exercise you engage in, you'd do it.

So it's simple to sustain. Just do what you love. 'Playout' not 'workout.'

See that?

PS: Exercise has a whole lot to do with longevity. And this is something you definitely cannot afford to miss out on!

LESSONS AND TAKEAWAYS

- Exercise is great for your health,
- Exercise more- you'll live longer.
- Exercise has its' risks. Be cautious!
- Exercise can guard against the effects of chronic emotional stress.

QUESTIONS

1. What do you know about exercise and the human body?

_____

_____

_____

_____

_____

_____

_____

_____

2. What activities would you engage in as acts of
   exercise? Choose activities that make you
   comfortable and write them out.

_____

_____

_____

_____

_____

_____

_____

_____

3. What are your reasons for choosing your answers in
   (2) above?

_____

_____

_____

_____

4. Since exercise makes you bigger and smarter, how many minutes of your week are you willing to commit to exercising?

_____

_____

_____

_____

5. What exercise activities make you feel uncomfortable? Write them out.

_____

_____

_____

_____

6. Has anyone asked you to exercise with them? What's your decision as regards that?

_____

_____

_____

_____

7. Imagine exercising, by doing what you love to do and loving how you feel, both on the inside and outside. How often would you like to move and feel like this?

_____

_____

_____

_____

8. Are there other activities you might want to try out? List them out.

_____

_____

_____

_____

_____

_____

_____

_____

ACTION STEPS

- Engage only in activities that are energizing and fun to you.
- Do not overdo any of these activities. Stop when you are no longer comfortable.
- Be consistent in your exercise, on a daily or weekly basis.
- Set targets, and reward yourself whenever you meet your set target.

CHECKLIST

- If you do not enjoy the activities you engage it, you won't be able to sustain it.
- Pair your exercise with music. It allows you relax. Find out the songs that get you to loosen and liven up.
- Remember to stay hydrated.

CHAPTER SIX: STRESS LESS

Chronic stress has a lot of negative impacts on your health and wellbeing. Increased inflammation, depression, shorter life span, etc., are some of the negative effects of chronic stress.

Surprisingly, stress isn't just about what happens to us, as individuals, but more about our reaction to the things that happen to us. These reactions of ours are founded on our lifestyles and beliefs. Hence, your perception of stress plays a greater role than what is actually happening in your life.

And although you cannot always change the things that happen to you, you can control your reactions to them much more than you know. By so doing, you heal better, and live longer.

LESSONS & TAKEAWAYS
- Stress comes primarily not just from what happens to us but, more important, how we react to what happens to us.
- If you feel stressed, you are stressed.
- Managing stress more effectively can beneficially affect our health.

- Eat well, love more, move more; and you'd stress less!

QUESTIONS

1. How many times do you feel stressed in the course of the week?

   _____

   _____

   _____

   _____

2. How much time do you spend on social media weekly? Why?

   _____

   _____

   _____

   _____

3. Do you engage in meditation regularly?

   _____

   _____

4. Meditation alone can actually change your genes. How much of your phone are you willing to drop and replace with meditation, daily?

_____

_____

_____

_____

5. What stress reduction techniques do you find convenient?

_____

_____

_____

_____

6. You need an hour of stress reduction techniques practiced daily to reverse chronic diseases. How do you plan on fitting this into your schedule?

_____

_____

_____

_____

7. The goal is to feel peaceful and relaxed. How do you feel?

_____

_____

_____

_____

ACTION STEPS

- Meditate during your downtime. Drop your phone.

- Practice micro-moments of positivity.

- Practice mindfulness.

- Keep your breath natural and through the nose whenever possible.

CHECKLIST

- Don't strain while practicing the stress management techniques.

- If it begins to hurt, discontinue what you're doing.

- Meditate in a well-ventilated room.

CHAPTER SEVEN: LOVE MORE

As a human being, the quality of your life is determined by how you love, and how you are loved, in return. There is an indispensable need for a real-time connection and fellowship with others.

Many, today, suffer from loneliness and depression, which have far reaching, negative consequences on your health and wellbeing. Nothing else has so much impact on your wellbeing and survival like loneliness does. Similarly, increase in the rates of suicide around the world show that loneliness is a serious epidemic that needs to be nipped in the bud.

You don't have to end like the rest. You can combat this ill via love and intimacy.

Let me walk you through this.

LESSONS AND TAKEAWAYS
- There is a primary need for authentic connection and community is primal.
- Loneliness causes chronic emotional stress and over-activation of the sympathetic nervous system.

- Love and intimacy can heal.
- There is a deep hunger for a sense of real intimacy.

QUESTIONS

1. Do you have anyone who really cares for, and loves you?

   _____

2. If your response to (1) above is yes, write out who this person(s) is/ are to you?

   _____

   _____

   _____

   _____

3. If your response to (1) above is No, write out what you suppose the problem is.

   _____

   _____

   _____

   _____

4. Have you ever considered participating in a support group?

_____

_____

_____

_____

5. How well do you love?

_____

_____

_____

_____

6. How often do you receive love from people, pets, etc?

_____

_____

_____

_____

7. How much time do you spend on social media daily? How do you feel afterwards?

_____

_____

_____

_____

ACTION STEPS

- Separate your thoughts from your feelings.
- Pay attention to the way you feel and express it.
- Be compassionate. Listen!

CHECKLIST

- Try not to judge or criticize.
- Be silent when listening to others.
- Avoid offering advice that was never solicited.

CHAPTER EIGHT: THE ORNISH KITCHEN/ TRUE LOVE RECIPES

For you to function at your best, you need to be properly nourished. Here, you'll meet with a whole lot of recipes that offer you taste, balance, nutrient and simplicity.

What's more? They are all in tandem with the guidelines of the lifestyle medicine program.

Whether it's breakfast or soups, salads or beverages; you're duly covered.

Enjoy!

QUESTIONS

1. Do you have breakfast regularly?

   _____

2. If your response to (1) above is yes, what factors have hitherto influenced your choice of meals?

   _____

   _____

_____

_____

3. If your response to (1) above is No, write out your
   reason for skipping your morning meals. Is that
   reason still valid?

   _____

   _____

   _____

   _____

4. Take a look at the recipes under breakfast. Which
   would you like to try today?

   _____

   _____

   _____

   _____

5. Soups or Salads?

   _____

   _____

   _____

   _____

6. Is your kitchen well stocked with the right set of foods? What will it cost you to dispose unhealthy foods like saturated fat and the likes?

_____

_____

_____

_____

ACTION STEPS

- Determine today to have a well-stocked kitchen.
- Stock your refrigerator only with healthy and fresh food.
- Follow the two weeks of recommended packaged foods, starting from tomorrow.

CHECKLIST

- Take stock of your kitchen staples.
- Keep a well-stocked pantry.

CPSIA information can be obtained
at www.ICGtesting.com
Printed in the USA
BVHW040914120320
574764BV00007B/626